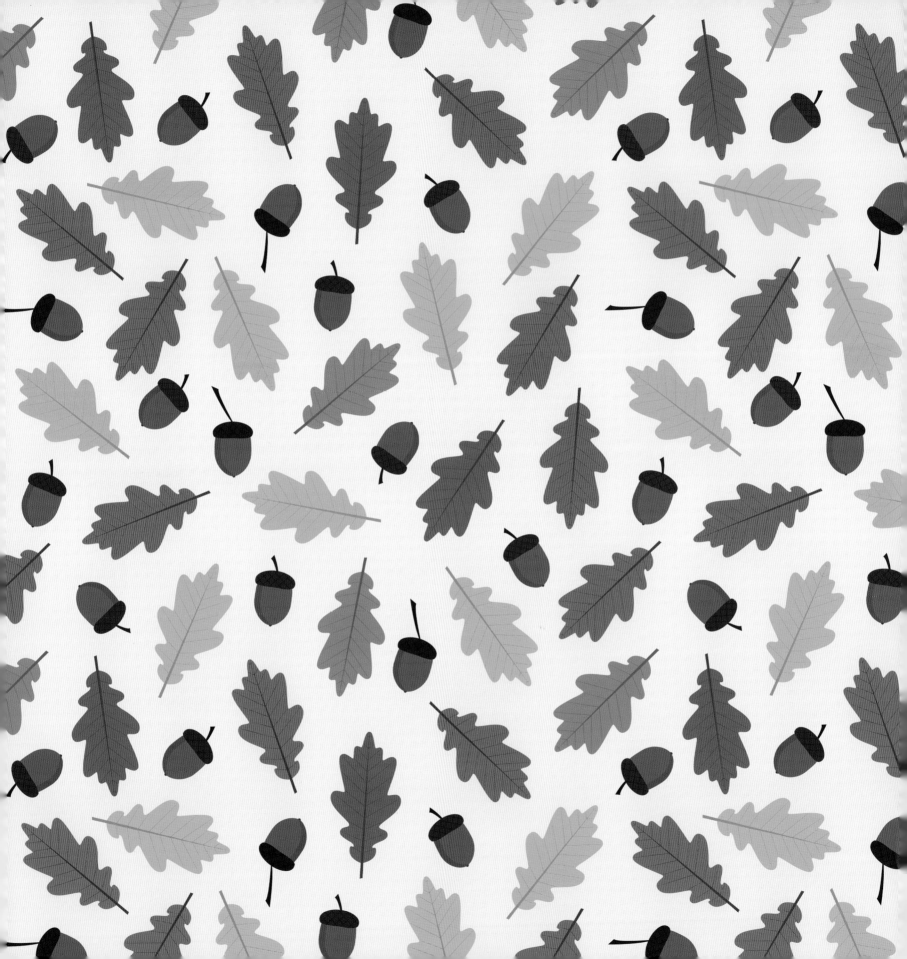

IMAGINE THAT™

Licensed exclusively to Imagine That Publishing Ltd
Tide Mill Way, Woodbridge, Suffolk, IP12 1AP, UK
www.imaginethat.com
Copyright © 2019 Imagine That Group Ltd
Endpapers © Tetiana Maltseva/Shutterstock.com
All rights reserved
0 2 4 6 8 9 7 5 3 1
Manufactured in China

Written by Eilidh Rose
Illustrated by Lisa Alderson

ISBN 978-1-78958-593-3

A catalogue record for this book is available from the British Library

Mummy's Near

Written by Eilidh Rose

Illustrated by Lisa Alderson

Curled up in a nest in an old oak tree, lived
Mummy Squirrel and her baby, Little Squirrel.

Little Squirrel was
scared to leave the nest
without his mummy.

'Don't be scared,
Little Squirrel.
Mummy's near,' she
said softly to her baby.

With his mummy's encouragement, Little Squirrel went to explore the tree and saw lots of interesting creatures!

Little Squirrel wanted to play with the baby squirrels who were crunching the crisp autumn leaves, but they were all bigger than him.

'Don't be scared, Little Squirrel. Mummy's near,' Mummy Squirrel said softly to her baby.

So Little Squirrel went to play with the bigger squirrels – and he had lots of fun!

Little Squirrel wanted to collect the juicy acorns that were hanging nearby, but there was a scary-looking bird.

'Don't be scared, Little Squirrel.
Mummy's near,' Mummy Squirrel
said softly to her baby.

Carefully, Little Squirrel collected a big pawful of acorns. They were delicious!

Little Squirrel wanted to visit his best friend, Little Owl, but he didn't know which branches to run along.

'Don't be scared, Little Squirrel. Mummy's near,' Mummy Squirrel said softly to her baby.

With a little help, Little Squirrel found the quickest way to get to Little Owl's nest!

One day, Little Squirrel came rushing home and ran straight into his mummy's arms. He told her that a big cat had chased him all the way home.

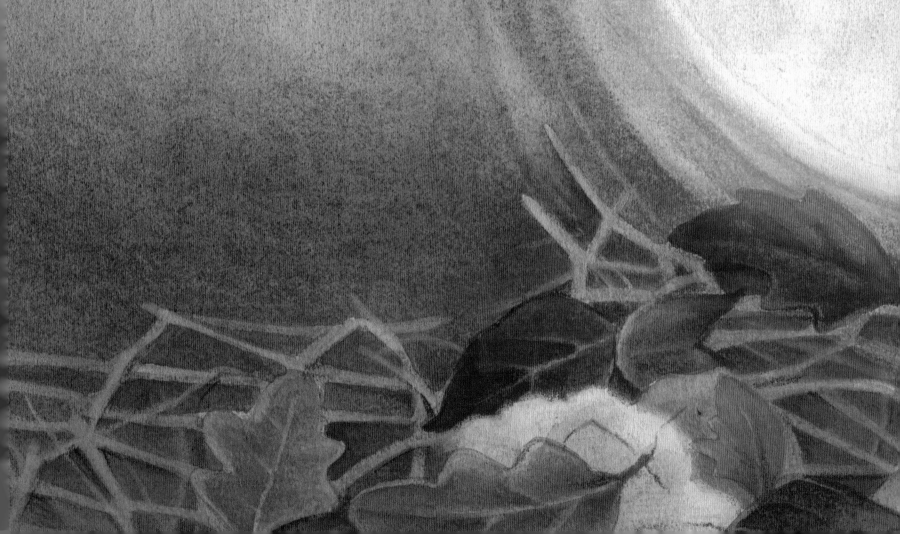

'Don't be scared, Little Squirrel. I'm very proud of you for being so brave and trying lots of new things by yourself,' Mummy Squirrel said softly to her baby.

'But, if ever you need me,
I will always be near.'

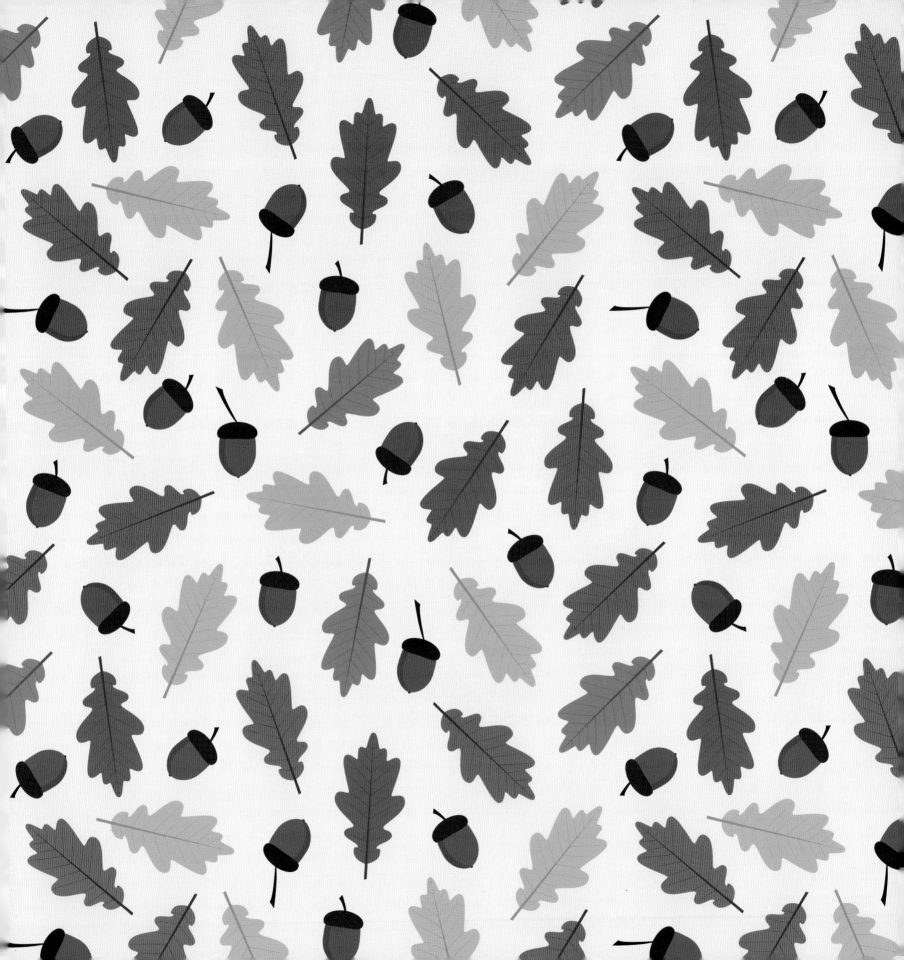